ROCK & POP

Grade 3

VOCALS

TRINITY
COLLEGE LONDON

THE EXAM AT A GLANCE

For your Rock & Pop exam you will need to perform a set of **three songs** and one of the **Session skills** assessments, either **Playback** or **Improvising**. You can choose the order in which you play your set-list.

Song 1

Choose a song from this book

OR from www.trinityrock.com

Song 2

Choose a different song from this book

OR from www.trinityrock.com

OR perform a song you have chosen yourself: this could be your own cover version or a song you have written. It should be at the same level as the songs in this book. See the website for detailed requirements.

Song 3: Technical focus

Choose one of the Technical focus songs from this book, which cover three specific technical elements.

Session skills

Choose either **Playback** or **Improvising**.

When you are preparing for your exam please check on **www.trinityrock.com** for the most up-to-date information and requirements as these can change from time to time.

CONTENTS

The CD can be used in a computer to access printable sheet music for certain songs in alternative keys, so you can choose the one which best suits your voice.

Trinity College London's Rock & Pop syllabus and supporting publications have been devised and produced in association with Faber Music and Peters Edition London.

Trinity College London
Registered office:
89 Albert Embankment
London SE1 7TP UK
T + 44 (0)20 7820 6100
F + 44 (0)20 7820 6161
E music@trinitycollege.co.uk
www.trinitycollege.co.uk

Registered in the UK. Company no. 02683033
Charity no. 1014792
Patron HRH The Duke of Kent KG

Copyright © 2012 Trinity College London
First published in 2012 by Trinity College London

Second impression, October 2012

Cover and book design by Chloë Alexander
Brand development by Andy Ashburner @ Caffeinehit (www.caffeinehit.com)
Photographs courtesy of Rex Features Limited.
Printed in England by Caligraving Ltd

Audio produced, mixed and mastered by Tom Fleming
Vocal arrangements by Oliver Weeks
Backing tracks arranged by Tom Fleming
Vocal Consultant: Heidi Pegler
Musicians
Vocals: Bo Walton, Brendan Reilly & Alison Symons
Keyboards: Oliver Weeks
Guitar & Bass: Tom Fleming
Bass: Ben Hillyard
Drums: George Double
Studio Engineer: Joel Davies www.thelimehouse.com

All rights reserved

ISBN: 978-0-85736-257-5

SONGS UMBRELLA

TRACK 1 demo TRACK 2 backing TRACK 3 backing higher key

Rihanna
Words and Music by Christopher Stewart, Shawn Carter, Terius Nash and Thaddis Harrell

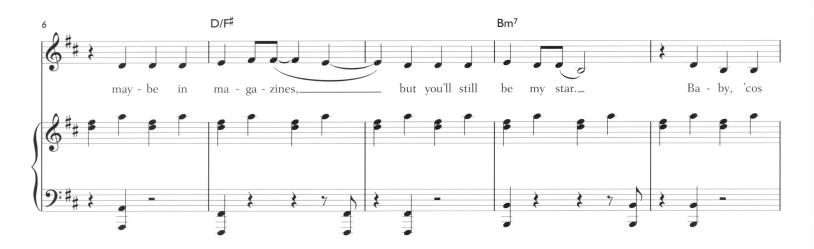

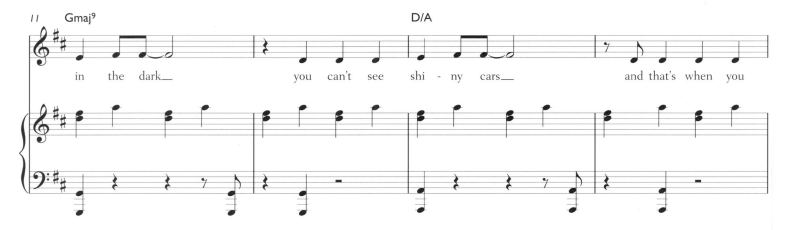

Alternative higher key available from the CD in this book

SONGS SUPER TROUPER

TRACK 4 demo TRACK 5 backing TRACK 6 backing lower key

ABBA
Words and Music by Benny Andersson and Björn Ulvaeus

♩ = 120 **Disco pop**

I was sick and tired of ev-'ry-thing when I called__ you last night from Glas __ gow,

all I do is eat and sleep and sing, wish-ing ev-'ry show was the last___ show.

Alternative lower key available from the CD in this book

SONGS

I ONLY WANT TO BE WITH YOU

Dusty Springfield
Words and Music by Mike Hawker and Ivor Raymonde

don't know what it is that makes me love you so,___ I on-ly know I nev-er wan-na

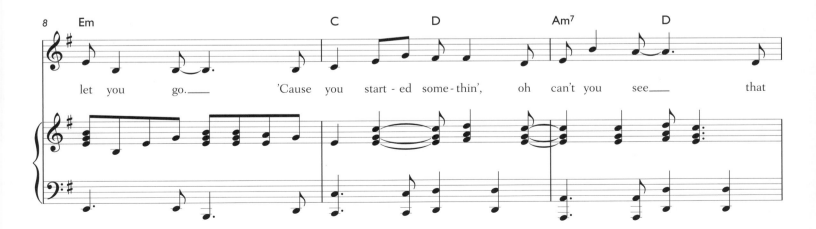

let you go.___ 'Cause you start-ed some-thin', oh can't you see___ that

Alternative higher key available from the CD in this book

BAND OPTION

SONGS JOHN BARLEYCORN

Trad.
Words and Music Trad.

there they made a solemn oath on poor John Barleycorn. They hired men with their crabtree sticks to cut him skin from bone, and the miller, he served him worse than that for he ground him beneath two stones.

WHAT A WONDERFUL WORLD

In your exam, you will be assessed on the following technical elements:

1 Grace notes

Bars 25 and 29 contain grace notes (♪), also known as 'crushed' notes, which are printed in small type next to the main notes. These are fast notes which should be sung just before the main note. You should be able to hear them clearly but they should not interrupt the flow of the music.

Be aware that the grace note in bar 25 is below the main note whereas the one in bar 29 is above.

2 Co-ordination with the accompaniment

'What A Wonderful World' is in $\frac{12}{8}$. This means that there are four ♩. beats in a bar, which are subdivided into ♪♪♪ notes. Most of the song is accompanied by ♪ notes. Listen to these and place your notes accurately over the top.

In bars 27 and 28 there is a new rhythm which uses consecutive ♩ notes:

This rhythm cuts across the ♩. beat. Practise it slowly at first, counting a ♪ beat, until the rhythm feels natural. This passage is marked 'freely' so, once you feel secure, the rhythm need not be precise.

If you are singing with the backing track, you will need to practise with it to make sure you are in time with the accompaniment.

3 Sustaining long notes

Hold the long notes in bars 9–10, 25–26 and 29–30 for their full lengths. Make sure that you take a good breath at the beginning of each of these phrases and sing through to the end of the phrase without taking an extra breath. Use plenty of support so that the long notes do not go out of tune or fade out.

WHAT A WONDERFUL WORLD

Louis Armstrong
Words and Music by George David Weiss and Bob Thiele

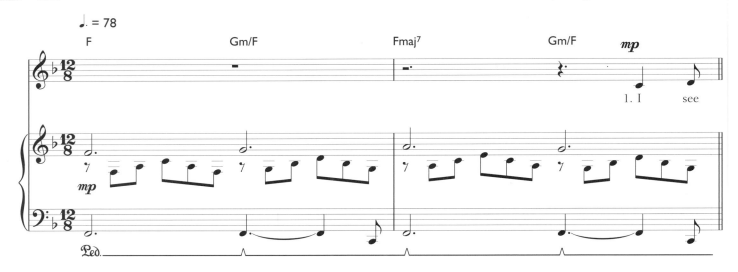

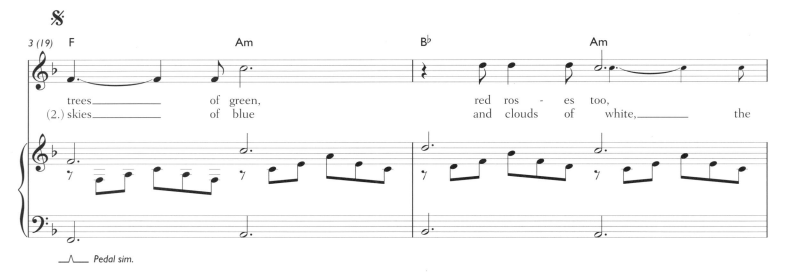

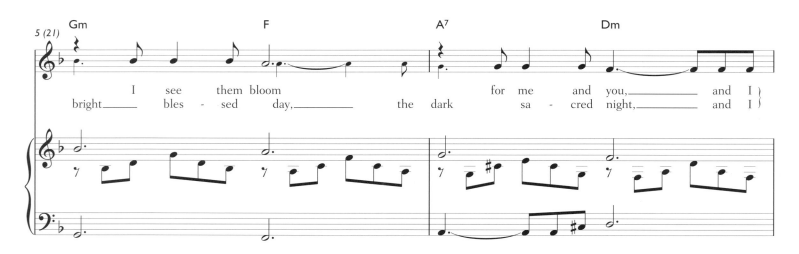

Alternative lower key available from the CD in this book

YOUR PAGE

NOTES

ALL DAY AND ALL OF THE NIGHT

In your exam, you will be assessed on the following technical elements:

1 Rhythmic precision

'All Day And All Of The Night' does not start on the first beat of the bar, but on a pick-up note on the last ♪ of the bar. Listen to the intro and then count through the guitar riff to help you come in on the pick-up. Listen carefully to the guitar riff: you start by singing exactly the same rhythm.

There is a long instrumental passage from bars 25–36. Count carefully and come in with confidence. Make sure you remain musically involved in the performance during this instrumental break.

2 Breathing

Plan where to breathe in this song. There are a lot of rests, but try not to breathe in all of them or the song may sound disjointed. Be sure not to breathe in the middle of a phrase. You could take a breath in bar 14 after the word 'alright' so you have enough strength and energy to *crescendo* through the word 'side', or you could take a big breath in bar 12 and sing the whole phrase in one breath. Keep relaxed when you take big breaths.

3 Dynamic range

This song should be big and bold. The dynamics range from *mf* (*mezzo forte* = moderately loud) to *f* (*forte* = loud). The climax of the song is reached at bars 14–16, after a *crescendo* (◁‾‾‾). Practise the *crescendo* so that you can make it smooth and gradual. Hold the final long note in bars 15–16 for its full value.

BAND OPTION

ALL DAY AND ALL OF THE NIGHT

The Kinks
Words and Music by Ray Davies

♩ = 136 **Rock**

on-ly time I feel al-right_ is by your_ side._____

Girl, I want to be with you all of the___ time, all day and all of the night.

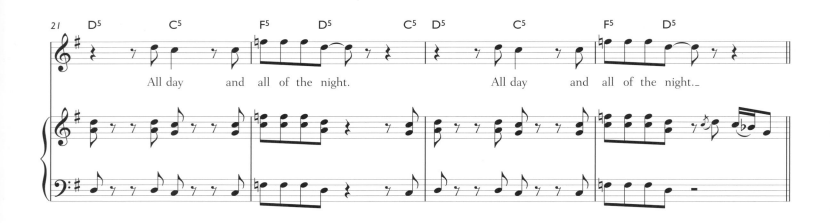

All day and all of the night. All day and all of the night._

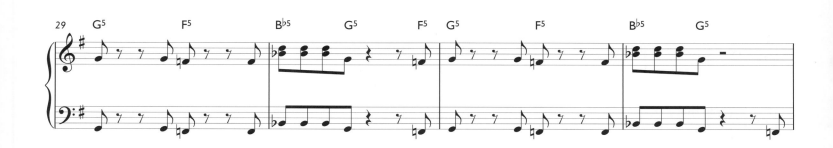

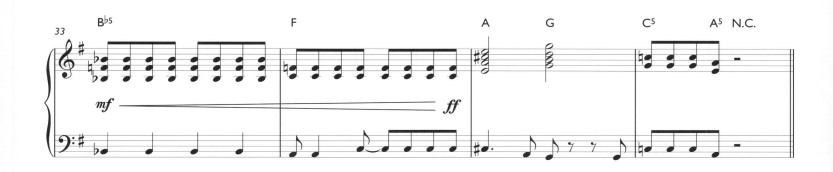

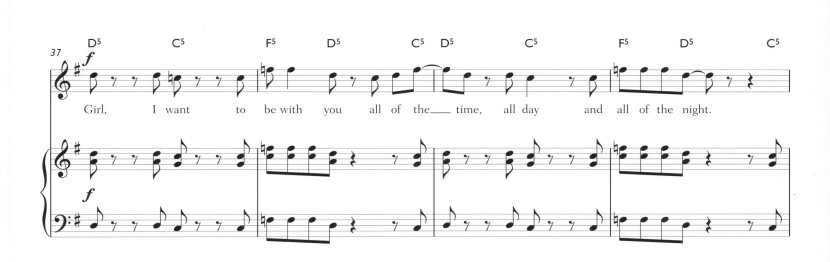

Girl, I want to be with you all of the____ time, all day and all of the night.

All day and all of the night. All day and all of the night.

ABOUT THE SONGS

UMBRELLA

Rihanna

Rihanna's third album *Good Girl Gone Bad,* released in 2007, turned her into an international star, with the single 'Umbrella' being a global smash hit.

Dominating pop music and fashion all over the world, Rihanna now holds the record as the only female artist of the past ten years to have ten number one hits in the US, as well as being the youngest soloist to do so.

'Umbrella' has a two-in-a-bar feel. The vocals start on a pick-up note on the last ♩ of the bar. Listen to the 2 bars count-in and count **1 2 3 4 1 2 3** before your entry.

There are a lot of words in this song, so try speaking the text several times before you sing. Articulate the consonants clearly – they will give the song energy and enable the listener to understand you more easily.

The vocal part is quite independent of the accompaniment so you need to be confident and secure when you are pitching the notes.

Remember that if this key doesn't suit your voice there is an alternative version in a higher key available from the CD in this book.

'*When* the *sun* shines *we'll* shine *together*'

SUPER TROUPER

ABBA

The Swedish pop quartet ABBA shot to fame after winning the Eurovision song contest in 1974; they went on to be the most successful pop band of the 1970s. Much of this was down to the song-writing partnership of two of their band members – Benny Andersson and Björn Ulvaeus.

'Super Trouper' is the title track of ABBA's 1980 album. The name 'Super Trouper' refers to the large spotlights used in stadium concerts. Like many of their songs, it has imaginative instrumentation, a catchy melody and instantly recognisable vocal harmonies. The song combines a carefree upbeat mood with a tinge of bittersweet sadness. In 1999 a musical, *Mamma Mia!*, featuring many of ABBA's most popular songs, was staged in London. The show is now running all over the world and a hugely successful film adaptation was released in 2008.

PERFORMANCE · HINTS & TIPS ·

Make sure that you keep a steady beat in this song – it is very easy to rush the ♪ notes. Some notes are marked with slurs (⌒). Sing the slurred notes as smoothly as you can. The other notes should be separated.

Hold the long notes for their full length: make sure that you take a good breath and use plenty of support so that they do not go out of tune or fade out. There is a pause (𝄐) on the last note of the song: be ready for this note and hold it for a little longer than four beats.

Remember that if this key doesn't suit your voice there is an alternative version in a lower key available from the CD in this book.

'*Somewhere* in *the* crowd *there's* you'

I ONLY WANT TO BE WITH YOU

Dusty Springfield

Dusty Springfield (1939–1999) was born Mary O'Brien. She began her career by singing with her brother Dion in The Springfields and then went on to have a long career as a solo singer. She had a distinctive, sultry sound rooted in black soul music – this led to her being dubbed the White Queen of Soul. With her trendy clothes, heavy eye makeup and peroxide blonde hair, she became a pop icon of the Swinging Sixties. Between 1964 and 1970 she was one of the most successful British female performers, with 18 singles in the charts.

The upbeat pop hit 'I Only Want To Be With You' (1963) was Dusty Springfield's first solo single. Her last chart success was with the Pet Shop Boys in the late 1980s.

'I Only Want To Be With You' needs a lively beat and rhythmic drive throughout. Work out where to breathe – making sure that you don't breathe mid-phrase. The song is mostly made up of two-bar phrases. You could breathe after each of the two-bar phrases, or you could take bigger breaths and sing through to make four-bar phrases. Try to avoid becoming tense when you take big breaths.

Look out for the accidentals in the middle section (bars 17–19): make sure that you pitch the notes securely.

Remember that if this key doesn't suit your voice there is an alternative version in a higher key available from the CD in this book.

'Ever *since* we *met* you've *had* a *hold* on *me*'

JOHN BARLEYCORN

Traffic

'John Barleycorn' is an English folk ballad with a long history dating back to the 16th century. This song – like all songs in the ballad tradition – tells a story. Nobody is really sure who John Barleycorn was, but one idea is that the name represents alcoholic drinks made from barley – a type of corn. There have been many versions of this song, by both folk singers and rock musicians. The 1960s rock band Traffic even named one of their best-selling albums after it – *John Barleycorn Must Die*.

'John Barleycorn' tells a story. There are many opportunities for characterisation during the story: use these to inject drama into the song.

There are two main dynamic markings in 'John Barleycorn': $\textbf{mf}$ (*mezzo forte* = moderately loud) and $\textbf{mp}$ (*mezzo piano* = moderately quiet): the song moves between these two dynamics throughout. Make sure that the difference between $\textbf{mf}$ and $\textbf{mp}$ can be heard. There are two *crescendos* (⎯⎯◁), at bars 13 and 25. You should get gradually louder in these bars.

Some notes are marked with slurs (⌒) – in, for example, bar 9. Sing these notes as smoothly as you can. The other notes should be separated.

This song is also in the keyboards, guitar, bass and drums books, so you can get together and play it in a band.

'These *three* men *made* a *solemn* vow'

ABOUT THE SONGS

WHAT A WONDERFUL WORLD

Louis Armstrong

Louis Armstrong (1901–1971) was one of the most famous pioneers of jazz. Born in New Orleans, the jazz capital of the world, his first great success was as a virtuoso cornet and trumpet player in King Oliver's Creole Jazz Band during the 1920s; he then played for many years with his own Hot Five and Hot Seven ensembles. He was a great improviser, but also an influential singer with a distinctive, gravelly voice.

Armstrong's recording of 'What A Wonderful World' was first released as a single in 1968. He had two distinct audiences: jazz fans who revered him for his early innovations as a jazz improviser, and pop fans who admired his singing. By the end of his career he was widely regarded as being hugely influential in both jazz and pop music.

PERFORMANCE · HINTS & TIPS ·

'What A Wonderful World' is a song of contentment. Much of it is marked *p* (*piano* = quiet) or *mp* (*mezzo piano* = moderately quiet), so should be kept fairly quiet throughout. Aim for a warm sound in the louder section at bar 15.

The symbol at the end of bar 18 means *Dal Segno* (from the sign) and then to the Coda. When you reach the **D.% al Coda** in bar 18 you go back to the % sign (in bar 3) and sing this passage again until you reach 'To Coda' at the end of bar 24. You then jump to where it says 'Coda' to finish the song.

Look out for the accidentals on the second page. In both bars 12 and 14 there is a G♯, but in bar 13 there is a G♮. Make sure that you pitch these notes accurately.

Remember that if this key doesn't suit your voice there is an alternative version in a lower key available from the CD in this book.

'*They're* really *sayin* "I love *you*"'

ABOUT THE SONGS

ALL DAY AND ALL OF THE NIGHT

The Kinks

The Kinks were one of the most influential bands of the 1960s. A four-piece London Mod band, they produced short punchy songs, often with high quality lyrics written by their singer Ray Davies. Like many British bands of that time, they began as an R&B group but their style changed over their long career.

The Kinks had a string of hit singles during the 1960s, including 'All Day And All Of The Night', which is built upon a simple sliding power chord riff.

This song should be bold and confident, so sing out.

The vocal line often has the same rhythm as the keyboards so listen carefully and make sure that you are exactly in time with the keyboard part. It will also help you to pitch the notes.

Watch out for the accidentals.

This song is also in the keyboards, guitar, bass and drums books, so you can get together and play it in a band.

'Girl, *I want* to be *with* you. *all of* the *time*'

PLAYBACK

For your exam, you can choose either Playback or Improvising (see page 35). If you choose Playback, you will be asked to perform some music you have not seen or heard before.

In the exam, you will be given the song chart and the examiner will play a recording of the music. You will hear several two-bar or four-bar phrases on the recording: you should sing each of them straight back in turn. There's a rhythm track going throughout, which helps you keep in time. There should not be any gaps in the music.

In the exam you will have two chances to perform with the recording:
- First time – for practice
- Second time – for assessment.

You should listen to the audio, copying what you hear; you can also read the music from the song chart. Here are some practice song charts which are also on the CD in this book. The music is printed without text and may be sung to any vowel (with or without consonant) or to sol-fa. The examples can include accents so you may need to use consonants or scat words to make them obvious.

Don't forget that the Playback test can include requirements which may not be shown in these examples, including those from earlier grades. Check the parameters at www.trinityrock.com to prepare for everything which might come up in your exam.

'I really *like* the *way* music *looks* on *paper.* It *looks* like *art* to *me*'

Steve Vai

Practice playback 1

Practice playback 2

YOUR PAGE NOTES

SESSION SKILLS IMPROVISING

For your exam, you can choose either Playback (see page 32), or Improvising. If you choose to improvise, you will be asked to improvise over a backing track that you haven't heard before in a specified style.

In the exam, you will be given a song chart and the examiner will play a recording of the backing track. The backing track consists of a passage of music played on a loop. You should improvise a melody line over the backing track.

In the exam you will have two chances to perform with the recording:
- First time – for practice
- Second time – for assessment.

Here are some improvising charts for practice which are also on the CD in this book. The music is printed without text and may be sung to any vowel (with or without consonant) or to sol-fa.

Don't forget that the Improvising test can include requirements which may not be shown in these examples, including those from earlier grades. Check the parameters at www.trinityrock.com to prepare for everything which might come up in your exam.

Practice improvisation 1

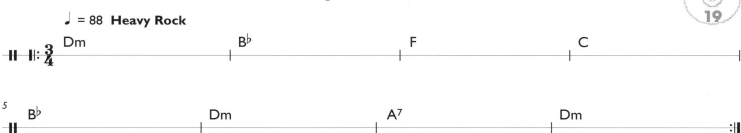

♩ = 88 **Heavy Rock**

Practice improvisation 2

♩ = 60 **Blues** (swung quavers)

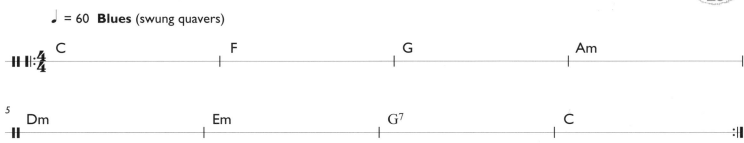

CHOOSING A SONG FOR YOUR EXAM

There are lots of options to help you choose your three songs for the exam. For Songs 1 and 2, you can choose a song which is:

- from this book
- from www.trinityrock.com

Or for Song 2 you can choose a song which is:

- sheet music from a printed or online source
- your own arrangement of a song or a song you have written yourself (see page 37).

You can perform the song unaccompanied or with a backing track (minus the solo voice). If you like, you can create a backing track yourself (or with friends).

For Grade 3, the song should last between one-and-half and three-and-a-half minutes, and the level of difficulty should be similar to your other songs. When choosing a song, think about:

- Does it work for my voice?
- Are there any technical elements that are too difficult for me? (If so, perhaps save it for when you do the next grade.)
- Do I enjoy singing it?
- Does it work with my other songs to create a good set-list?

SHEET MUSIC

You must always bring an original copy of the book or a download sheet with email certificate for each song you perform in the exam. If you choose to write your own song you must provide the examiner with a copy of the sheet music. Your music can be:

- a lead sheet with lyrics, chords and melody line
- a chord chart with lyrics
- a full score using conventional staff notation
- see page 37 for details on presenting a song you have written yourself.

The title of the song and your name should be on the sheet music.

HELP PAGES

WRITING YOUR OWN SONG

You can perform a song that you have written yourself for one of the choices in your exam. For Grade 3, your song should last between one-and-half and three-and-a-half minutes. It is sometimes difficult to know where to begin, so here are some suggestions for starting points:

- **A rhythm**: A short repeated rhythm will often underpin an entire song. Start by writing a couple of short rhythms here:

- **A riff**: A riff is a short rhythm which is repeated over and over. A short repeated riff will often underpin an entire song. Write a couple of riffs here:

WRITING YOUR SONG DOWN

Rock and pop music is often written as a **lead sheet** with the lyrics (if there are any), chords and a melody line.

You can, if you prefer, use a **graph** or **table** to represent your music, as long as it is clear to anyone else (including the examiner) how the song goes.

- **Instruments**: Which instruments will play your song? You could just use voice and keyboards or guitar, or you could add bass and drums and any other instruments.

There are plenty of other ways of starting: perhaps with a melody, chord sequence or a lyric.

You will also need to consider the **structure** of your song (verse and chorus, 12-bar blues, and son on) and the **style** it is in (blues, hard rock, etc.).

There are many choices to be made – which is why writing a song is such a rewarding thing to do.

SINGING IN A BAND

Singing in a band is exciting: it can be a lot of fun and, as with everything, the more you do it, the easier it gets. It is very different from performing on your own. Everyone contributes to the overall sound: the most important skill you need to develop is listening.

For a band to sound good, the players need to be 'together' – that mainly means keeping in time with each other, but also playing at the same volume, and with the same kind of feeling. Your relationship with the other band members is also important. Talk with them about the music you sing, the music you like, and what you'd like the band to achieve short-term and long-term.

Band rehearsals are important – you should not be late, tired or distracted by your mobile phone! Being positive makes a huge difference. Try to create a friendly atmosphere in rehearsals so that everybody feels comfortable trying out new things. Don't worry about making mistakes: that is what rehearsals are for.

'All Day and All Of The Night' (page 23) and 'John Barleycorn' (page 14) are arranged for band. You will find parts for keyboards, guitar, bass and drums in the other Trinity Rock & Pop Grade 3 books. Trinity offers exams for groups of musicians at various levels. The songs arranged for bands are ideal to include as part of a set-list for these exams. Have a look at the website for more details.

HINTS AND TIPS

- Record your practice sessions and listen carefully to the recordings. Which sections worked well and which had problems? How will you improve the sections with problems?

- In some songs you will play a supporting role; at other times you may take more of a lead. In both cases you need to listen to the overall group as well as to your own part. Be aware of how you affect the sound – every player should make their own distinct contribution to the overall sound.

- Nothing beats the thrill of performing live in front of an audience. Organise a gig for a few friends. It can be a small gig in someone's house – the important thing is to get used to performing in front of other people. Gigs can be nerve-wracking at first, but try to relax and enjoy them.

PERFORMING WITH BACKING TRACKS

The CD contains demos and backing tracks of all the songs in the book. The additional songs at www.trinityrock.com also come with demos and backing tracks.

- In your exam, you should perform with the backing track, or you can create your own (see below).
- The backing tracks begin with a click track, which sets the tempo and helps you start accurately.
- Be careful to balance the volume of the backing track against your voice.
- Listen carefully to the backing track to ensure you are singing in time.

If you are creating your own backing track here are some further tips:
- Make sure the sound quality is of a good standard.
- Think carefully about the instruments/sounds you are putting on the backing track.
- Avoid copying what you are singing on the backing track – it should support not duplicate.
- Do you need to include a click track at the beginning?

COPYRIGHT IN A SONG

If you are a singer or songwriter it is important to know about copyright. When someone writes a song or creates an arrangement they own the copyright (sometimes called 'the rights') to that version. The copyright means that other people cannot copy it, sell it, perform it in a concert, make it available online or record it without the owner's permission or the appropriate licence. When you write a song you automatically own the copyright to it, which means that other people cannot copy your work. But just as importantly, you cannot copy other people's work, or perform it in public without their permission or the appropriate licence.

Points to remember
- You can create a cover version of a song for an exam or other non-public performance.
- You cannot record your cover version and make your recording available to others (by copying it or uploading it to a website) without the appropriate licence.
- You own the copyright of your own original song, which means that no one is allowed to copy it.
- You cannot copy someone else's song without their permission or the appropriate licence.
- If you would like to use somebody else's words in your own song you must check if they are in copyright and, if so, we recommend you confirm with the author that they are happy for the words to be used as lyrics.
- Materials protected by copyright can normally be used as lyrics in our examinations as these are private performances under copyright law. The examiner may ask you the name of the original author in the exam.
- When you present your own song to the examiner make sure you include the title, the names of any writers and the source of your lyrics.

ALSO AVAILABLE

Trinity College London Rock & Pop examinations 2012-2017 are also available for:

Bass Initial
ISBN: 978-0-85736-227-8

Bass Grade 1
ISBN: 978-0-85736-228-5

Bass Grade 2
ISBN: 978-0-85736-229-2

Bass Grade 3
ISBN: 978-0-85736-230-8

Bass Grade 4
ISBN: 978-0-85736-231-5

Bass Grade 5
ISBN: 978-0-85736-232-2

Bass Grade 6
ISBN: 978-0-85736-233-9

Bass Grade 7
ISBN: 978-0-85736-234-6

Bass Grade 8
ISBN: 978-0-85736-235-3

Drums Initial
ISBN: 978-0-85736-245-2

Drums Grade 1
ISBN: 978-0-85736-246-9

Drums Grade 2
ISBN: 978-0-85736-247-6

Drums Grade 3
ISBN: 978-0-85736-248-3

Drums Grade 4
ISBN: 978-0-85736-249-0

Drums Grade 5
ISBN: 978-0-85736-250-6

Drums Grade 6
ISBN: 978-0-85736-251-3

Drums Grade 7
ISBN: 978-0-85736-252-0

Drums Grade 8
ISBN: 978-0-85736-253-7

Guitar Initial
ISBN: 978-0-85736-218-6

Guitar Grade 1
ISBN: 978-0-85736-219-3

Guitar Grade 2
ISBN: 978-0-85736-220-9

Guitar Grade 3
ISBN: 978-0-85736-221-6

Guitar Grade 4
ISBN: 978-0-85736-222-3

Guitar Grade 5
ISBN: 978-0-85736-223-0

Guitar Grade 6
ISBN: 978-0-85736-224-7

Guitar Grade 7
ISBN: 978-0-85736-225-4

Guitar Grade 8
ISBN: 978-0-85736-226-1

Keyboards Initial
ISBN: 978-0-85736-236-0

Keyboards Grade 1
ISBN: 978-0-85736-237-7

Keyboards Grade 2
ISBN: 978-0-85736-238-4

Keyboards Grade 3
ISBN: 978-0-85736-239-1

Keyboards Grade 4
ISBN: 978-0-85736-240-7

Keyboards Grade 5
ISBN: 978-0-85736-241-4

Keyboards Grade 6
ISBN: 978-0-85736-242-1

Keyboards Grade 7
ISBN: 978-0-85736-243-8

Keyboards Grade 8
ISBN: 978-0-85736-244-5

Vocals Initial
ISBN: 978-0-85736-254-4

Vocals Grade 1
ISBN: 978-0-85736-255-1

Vocals Grade 2
ISBN: 978-0-85736-256-8

Vocals Grade 3
ISBN: 978-0-85736-257-5

Vocals Grade 4
ISBN: 978-0-85736-258-2

Vocals Grade 5
ISBN: 978-0-85736-259-9

Vocals Grade 6 (female voice)
ISBN: 978-0-85736-263-6

Vocals Grade 6 (male voice)
ISBN: 978-0-85736-260-5

Vocals Grade 7 (female voice)
ISBN: 978-0-85736-264-3

Vocals Grade 7 (male voice)
ISBN: 978-0-85736-261-2

Vocals Grade 8 (female voice)
ISBN: 978-0-85736-265-0

Vocals Grade 8 (male voice)
ISBN: 978-0-85736-262-9